The Sailing Quiz Book

Tony Crowley

ADLARD COLES LIMITED
8 Grafton Street, London W1

Adlard Coles Ltd
William Collins Sons & Co. Ltd
8 Grafton Street, London W1X 3LA

First published in Great Britain by
Adlard Coles Ltd 1986

Distributed in the United States of America
by Sheridan House, Inc.

British Library Cataloguing in Publication Data
Crowley, Tony
The sailing quiz book.
1. Sailing—Miscellanea
I. Title
797.1′24′076   GV811

ISBN 0-229-11780-5

Printed and bound in Great Britain by
Mackays of Chatham, Kent

INTRODUCTION

Welcome to *The Sailing Quiz Book*. The book is packed with quizzes, riddles, and puzzles concerning the many different aspects of sailing – there is even a personality test to help you to decide the best kind of sailing for you.

It is hoped that the book will be a source of interest, entertainment, and reference to all who enjoy sailing; a diversion for families during the off-season or when bad weather cancels the weekend cruise, or as a learning and revision aid for yachtsmen and women preparing for RYA examinations.

Answers to all the quizzes are provided at the back of the book, but have a go and see if you can puzzle out the correct solution before turning to this section.

The contents do not follow any special order but the longer quizzes have been organised into three sections:

Force 1 to 4: Fairly easy
Force 5 to 7: Medium difficulty
Force 8 to 10: Heavy going

Finally, several short but useful microcomputer programs will be found at the back of the book, and these include a morse code training program.

PART 1 Force 1 to 4
Light airs to a moderate breeze

SAILING

Here is a short quiz to test your knowledge of basic sailing terms.

1. What are the three main points of sailing (in relation to the wind)?
   (a)..................... (b)..................... (c).....................

2. What terms are used to describe the situation when
   (a) the wind is dead ahead? ....
   (b) the wind is before (just ahead of) the beam? ....
   (c) the wind is abaft (just behind) the beam?.....................
   (d) the wind is dead astern? ....
   (e) the boat is running with the wind on the same side as the boom?
   ....

3. What call should be given to warn members of the crew that the boat is
   (a) going to change tack – that is, change direction so the bows pass through the wind?
   ....
   (b) going to gybe – that is, change direction so the stern passes through the wind?
   ....

4. What call is given as a warning at the time the boat actually
   (a) changes tack? ....
   (b) gybes?...

5. What order is given to the helmsman so that he or she
   (a) moves the boat's head closer to the direction of the wind (to windward)?
   ....
   (b) keeps the boat on its present course?
   ....
   (c) moves the boat's head away from the wind (to leeward)?
   ....

WORDSEARCH

Hidden among this panel of letters are the names of ten different parts of a sail. They run in all directions: forwards, backwards, up, down, and diagonally. *Some cross each other*. When you have managed to find them, use the diagram to locate their correct positions.

Q	T	E	J	R	H	M	B	O	J
N	D	X	A	E	J	E	O	L	U
E	R	R	A	I	W	H	N	Q	S
N	A	D	C	E	N	E	P	E	N
P	O	I	N	T	S	T	L	S	E
O	B	R	N	K	Y	G	U	C	T
P	D	O	C	L	N	I	F	S	T
T	A	F	E	I	A	S	F	A	A
M	E	W	R	J	B	D	C	H	B
R	H	C	E	E	L	K	U	A	W
T	O	O	F	P	L	A	D	B	J

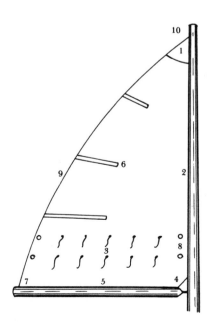

SEATALK 1

Like many occupations, seafaring has a language of its own. A few terms are found in general use, e.g. changing tack, but the majority remain a mystery to the landlubber. Can you provide a suitable translation for the following nautical verbs?

1. To batten down. . . . .
2. To fend off . . . .
3. To gather way . . . .
4. To heel. . . . .
5. To labour. . . . .
6. To launch . . . .
7. To log . . . .
8. To make fast . . . .
9. To make sail. . . . .
10. To pay out. . . . .
11. To scull. . . . .
12. To stand on . . . .
13. To stow. . . . .
14. To unship . . . .
15. To weigh . . . .

DIFFERENCES 1

What is the difference between

1. A boat and a ship?
2. A sloop and a cutter?
3. A ketch and a yawl?
4. A brig and a brigantine?
5. A barque and a barquentine?

nightwatch

'I'm not saying it was rough, but for three days I wore a porthole as a collar.'

QUICK CROSSWORD

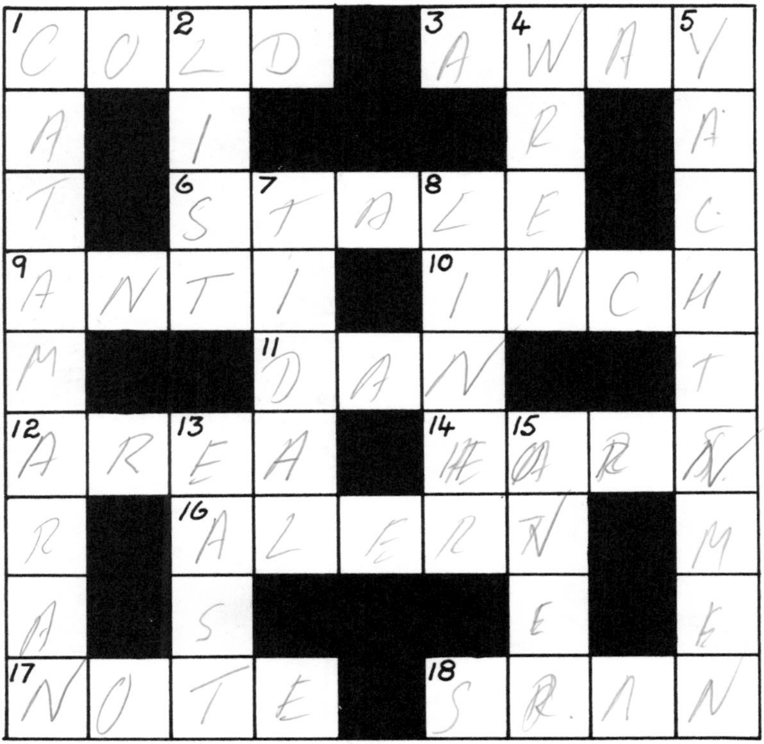

Clues across:

1. Might describe a spell of weather (4)
3. 'Haul .... Joe!' (4)
6. Air in an unventilated space (5)
9. .... fouling paint (4)
10. To move forward gradually (4)
11. A floating marker buoy (3)
12. By which sails are measured (4)
14. You need them when caught in fog (4)
16. On your guard and ready for action (5)
17. A brief entry in the log book (4)
18. A wire strop along the gaff (4)

Clues down:

1. A vessel with two hulls (9)
2. Permanently heeled over (4)
4. A female naval rating (4)
5. Men (and women) who enjoy sailing (9)
7. Affected by the tides (5)
8. Large passenger vessel (5)
13. 180 degrees from West (4)
15. Aloft (4)

CAPSIZE

You are enjoying a pleasant evening's sail on a small dinghy in an estuary when a sudden gust of wind causes you to capsize. You have no crew with you. Which of the following steps would you take? Select 8 and place them in the order in which you would carry them out.

1. Lower all the sails
2. Fire a portable distress flare
3. Swim around to the centreboard
4. Free the mainsheet
5. Remove centreboard completely
6. Start bailing out the boat
7. Swim to the shore for help
8. Pull boat's head up to wind
9. Haul on the jib and use weight to right the boat
10. Climb up carefully onto the centreboard, keeping weight as close as possible to the hull
11. Swim to shore using mainsheet as towline
12. Give the boardsailing distress signal
13. Stay with the boat
14. Stand on the tip of the centreboard and jump up and down with as much force as possible
15. Remove rudder and tiller
16. Throw the end of the jib sheet over the side of the boat
17. Climb aboard as quickly as possible after falling into the water
18. Remove personal buoyancy-aid to aid body movements
19. Swim to the stern and check that the rudder is secure

1 ....   5 ....
2 ....   6 ....
3 ....   7 ....
4 ....   8 ....

CHART SYMBOLS 1

Twenty widely-used chart abbreviations for you to decipher. The first five concern the quality of the sea bottom in some way.

1. S ....
2. M ....
3. Sn ....
4. P ....
5. Wd ....
6. Wk ....
7. Bn ....
8. L B ....
9. Rk ....
10. Tr ....
11. M ....
12. L W ....
13. C G ....
14. Ch+ ....
15. vis ....
16. N B ....
17. Obscd ....
18. Ft ....
19. Ho ....
20. Lk ....

RIGHT WAY, WRONG WAY 1

1.

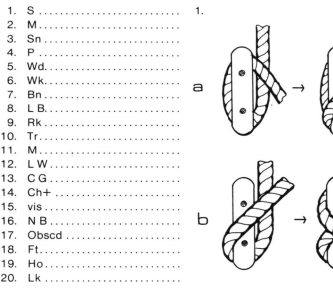

a →

OR

b →

2.

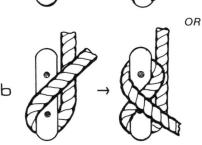

a

OR

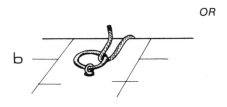

b

7

PERSONALITY

At great expense, Madame Zodiac has provided you with the character reading below. Unfortunately, she uses the same reading for all her clients. Look through the statements and indicate which ones you fully agree with, only partly agree with, or completely disagree with, by circling the numbers provided.

			Fully agree	Partly agree	Disagree
1.	(a)	You like going for long walks by yourself	2	1	0
	(b)	You like having your photograph taken	2	1	0
	(c)	You enjoy organising clubs or societies	2	1	0
	(d)	You always try to get along with others	2	1	0
2.	(a)	You usually avoid large crowds	2	1	0
	(b)	You enjoy acting or singing in front of an audience	2	1	0
	(c)	People often ask you for your advice	2	1	0
	(d)	You like to be with a group of people	2	1	0
3.	(a)	You prefer to sort out your own problems	2	1	0
	(b)	You'd wear a funny costume if it made people laugh	2	1	0
	(c)	You're good at suggesting how things should be done	2	1	0
	(d)	You hate missing a party, disco, or outing with friends	2	1	0
4.	(a)	You prefer to plan things your own way	2	1	0
	(b)	You can be a bit of a show-off	2	1	0
	(c)	You like giving orders and telling people what to do	2	1	0
	(d)	You enjoy most team games	2	1	0
5.	(a)	You often find that you prefer books to people	2	1	0
	(b)	You enjoy making speeches or giving talks	2	1	0
	(c)	You can take charge of things in an emergency	2	1	0
	(d)	When others are enjoying themselves you join in too	2	1	0
6.	(a)	You find you work best when you work alone	2	1	0
	(b)	You are never shy in front of strangers	2	1	0
	(c)	You quite enjoy having to make decisions for others	2	1	0
	(d)	You've always made friends quite easily	2	1	0

		Disagree Partly agree Fully agree

7. (a) You don't mind being left on your own   2 1 0
    (b) You like telling jokes or interesting stories   2 1 0
    (c) If people are wrong about something you soon
         tell them   2 1 0
    (d) You enjoy listening to other people's conversation   2 1 0

Add together the scores for the seven (a) items and then do the same with the (b), (c) and (d) items. A high (a) score means you will fall into the first category given on the answer page, with a high (b) score pointing to the second answer, and so on. Don't take it too seriously, however . . .

MEMORY BANK

How good is your memory? Study the items left lying on the deck on p. 27 for exactly one minute, and then turn back to this page to see how many you can remember.

1. *Bucket*
2. *Brush*
3. *Rope*
4. *Shackle*
5. *Buoy*
6. *Anchor*
7. *David*
8. *Nav Light*
9. *Boat flask*
10. *Sender*
11. *Pen Knife*
12. ....
13. ....
14. ....
15. ....

A CUTE ANGLE

A hand aboard a ship I knew
could measure angles fair and
*   true*
without a sextant or nautical aid,
how were those calculations made?

KNOTTY PROBLEM

a

From the knots, bends, and hitches illustrated, pick out the best one for the jobs listed below.

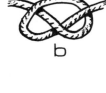

b

1. To join two lines of different size

2. To attach a line to a spar or rail (e.g. lifting up a bucket)

3. To make a simple stopper knot quickly

4. To connect two large mooring lines or hawsers

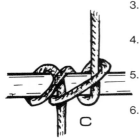

c

5. To prevent a line from *unreeving* through a block

6. To secure a light mooring line to a post

7. To join two lines of the same size

8. To lash something by line to a larger rope (e.g. anchor light)

d

9. To join a heaving line to a mooring rope

and finally . . .

10. What is the difference between a knot, a bend, and a hitch?

i

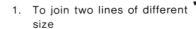

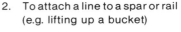

h

g

e

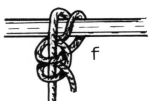

f

FLAG DAY

The International Code of Signals enables ships to communicate with each other or with a shore station, using morse code, letter codes, or flags. The letters and numbers are used individually or in combination to pass messages which have been coded according to an internationally agreed system. Individual letters of the alphabet are reserved for some of the more important signals. Although a small sailing vessel would not be expected to carry a full set of flags, the skipper should be able to identify the 26 main codes. With the aid of a reference book like *Reed's Nautical Almanac*, indicate the letters, morse code, and flags associated with the messages listed below. You might like to complete the flag diagrams with the correct colours.

Page 48 of *The Sailing Quiz Book* includes a microcomputer program to aid the learning of morse code.

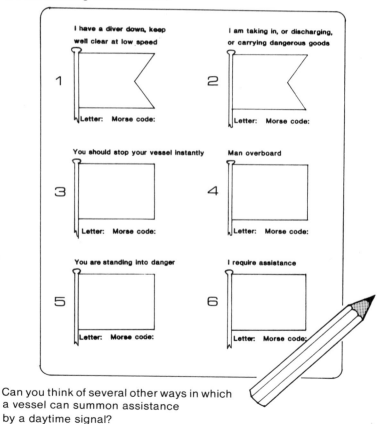

1. I have a diver down, keep well clear at low speed
   Letter: Morse code:

2. I am taking in, or discharging, or carrying dangerous goods
   Letter: Morse code:

3. You should stop your vessel instantly
   Letter: Morse code:

4. Man overboard
   Letter: Morse code:

5. You are standing into danger
   Letter: Morse code:

6. I require assistance
   Letter: Morse code:

Can you think of several other ways in which a vessel can summon assistance by a daytime signal?

STARGAZER

Few constellations remotely resemble the objects after which they are named, but deep-sea navigators find them useful in helping to locate specific stars. The pointers in the Plough (or Great Bear) used to locate the Pole Star are good examples of this.

Unscramble and identify the names of the constellations illustrated here.

1. ASIPACOESIA

    . . . .

2. MIGINE

    . . . .

3. CIRCUS

    . . . .

4. YARL

    . . . .

5. OLE

    . . . .

6. ARTUSU

    . . . .

7. NOORI

    . . . .

8. GUPSASE

    . . . .

9. NYSCUG

    . . . .

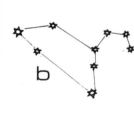

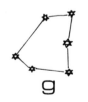

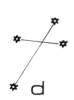

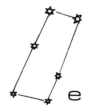

SURVIVAL

1. A shipmate has burnt her arm
    on a steam pipe. Do you
    - (a) cover the burn generously
      with grease?
    - (b) flush it with clean cold
      water?
    - (c) bandage the burn tightly?
    - (d) burst any blisters carefully?

2. You are left looking after some-
    one who is lying on the deck in
    a state of shock. Do you
    - (a) keep him cold?
    - (b) keep him talking?
    - (c) keep him warm?
    - (d) keep him walking?

3. Whilst operating equipment linked to the shore, a shipmate receives a
    severe electric shock and is now lying in contact with the machine.
    If possible, do you
    - (a) pull him away as quickly as possible?
    - (b) run for medical assistance?
    - (c) remove him from the machine with non-conductive material?
    - (d) switch off the current?

4. Your companion is suffering from frost-bite. Do you
    - (a) warm the affected area gently?
    - (b) apply a hot water bottle?
    - (c) plunge the affected area into hot water?
    - (d) rub the affected area with your hands?

5. If someone has stopped breathing, the first priority is
    - (a) to throw cold water in his/her face
    - (b) to get air into the lungs
    - (c) to get the heart pumping
    - (d) to deliver a sharp blow to the breastbone

HELP WANTED!

Which famous explorer inserted the following newspaper advert in
1900?
*Men wanted for hazardous journey. Small wages, bitter cold, constant
danger, safe return doubtful. Honour and recognition in case of success.
Apply: Box 100*

DEDUCTION

'I heard my clock strike ten minutes before the gun at the start of the race. It struck an odd, not an even number, and certainly more than once. Unfortunately my clock stopped at 4.55 p.m.'

What time did the race start?

OPPOSITES

What is the opposite of
1. Starboard....................
2. Deck........................
3. Stem........................
4. Let go!.....................
5. Head (of a sail)..............
6. Luff (of a sail) ....
7. Greenwich Meridian ....
8. Leeward....................
9. ENE ....
10. Astern ....
11. Tack ....
12. Abaft.......................
13. 4 points on port bow........
14. Forestay....................
15. Dead run....................
16. Crown (of anchor)...........
17. Crown (of block) ....
18. Pulpit.......................
19. Wake ....
20. Bowsprit....................
21. 'At the dip' ....
22. Hogging ....
23. Fore and aft..................
24. Head (of a flag) ....
25. Boom (tricky!) ....

RIGHT WAY, WRONG WAY 2

1.

a   OR   b

2.

a   OR   b

PART 2 Force 5 to 7
Fresh breeze to moderate gale

NOAH'S ARK

A ship is almost a floating zoo. See if you can identify the nautical association with the animals listed, e.g. cat and catwalk (a long, narrow walkway). In some cases, there are several items involved.

1. Bulldog	8. Dog	15. Mule
2. Bull	9. Duck	16. Otter
3. Butterfly	10. Goose	17. Pelican
4. Cat	11. Horse	18. Ram
5. Cock	12. Hound	19. Rat
6. Cow	13. Jackass	20. Swallow
7. Crow	14. Monkey	

DROPPING THE PICK

1. Why is it preferable to be moving slightly astern before the anchor is dropped?
2. How much scope or length of cable should be veered (let out) when anchoring?
3. What name is usually given to a second anchor and what is it used for?
4. What is the purpose of a tripping line?
5. Give several reasons why a boat might drag its anchor.
6. How can you check to see if the anchor is dragging?
7. Which bend is used to secure a rope warp to an anchor chain?
8. How do you show other vessels that you are at anchor?
9. What would you use an anchor's chum for?
10. You are approaching an anchorage or mooring and the engine has packed up. How do you approach under sail if the wind is (a) against the tide, and (b) with the tide?

HARD TACK

The yachts *Sea Slug* and *Ocean Snail* set off on different tacks to reach a buoy several miles away to the West. The wind is West by North – a point to the North of West – and occasionally backs or veers. *Sea Slug* starts off on the starboard tack whereas *Ocean Snail* chooses the port tack. Which yacht is more likely to reach the buoy first?

(a) *Sea Slug* (b) *Ocean Snail* (c) Neither yacht has any particular advantage

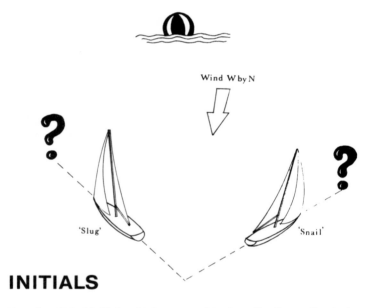

Wind W by N

'Slug'   'Snail'

INITIALS

Here is a list of initials which are used to describe the method of propulsion or the purpose of a vessel. See how many you can identify.

1. SS...
2. MV..
3. RMS ....
4. GTS...
5. OBO ....
6. RORO..
7. VLCC..
8. LNGC ....
9. ACV..
10. COMBI..

SEA JOBS

What occupations do (or did) the following usually perform on a merchant ship?

1. Sparks ....
2. Old man ....
3. Peggy ....
4. Lecky ....
5. Donkey...
6. Farmer ....
7. Lampy..
8. Chippy ....
9. Middy ....
10. Tiger ....

ALCOR

The next time you look at the Plough (or Great Bear) constellation of stars, see if you can spot a small star next to the middle star in the handle or tail

Pole Star

Tradition has it that this star (Alcor) was used as an eyesight test many centuries ago for men joining Arabian armies. The failure rate was high but that probably says more about the popularity of an Army career than its value as a sight test. It was certainly used by some sailing ship captains to check if a seaman's vision was good enough for steering by night.

When did you last have *your* sight tested?

NAVIGATION

This problem is presented for the benefit of those inland sailors who have never had to worry about tides and currents! The problem looks deceptively simple, but it is one which few people get right.

Imagine you are sailing towards an anchorage 5 miles to the North of your position. Your speed is 5 knots, but there is a current setting East at 4 knots. The diagram below shows your intended course and the direction of the current. Use the diagram to work out the *direction* in which you should steer to make the anchorage, and mark it up on the diagram. You can assume that the wind is behind you and there is no leeway. The distance between dots = 1 sea mile.

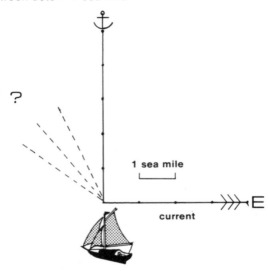

DIFFERENCES 2

What is the difference between

1. Mist and fog
2. Hawser-laid rope and cable-laid rope
3. A CQR anchor and a Danforth anchor
4. A reef knot and a granny knot
5. A backing wind and a veering wind
6. The fall and the standing part of a purchase or tackle
7. A nautical mile and a land mile
8. Serving a rope and whipping a rope
9. A shipbroker and a ship chandler
10. A jib stick and a whisker pole

BASIC RACING QUIZ

1. How many minutes before a race begins is the warning flag hoisted or broken out?
2. What additional flag is broken out five minutes later?
3. Why should a stop-watch be considered an essential aid to a racing yachtsman?
4. What happens if several yachts make a false start?
5. When does a yacht actually start a race?
6. What is the best tack on which to start a race?
7. What shape should a racing flag hoisted at the masthead be?
8. Within how many lengths of a mark should overlap be established in order to gain a manoeuvring advantage over the boat ahead?
9. What is an *intervening* overlap?
10. Two overlapping boats are close-hauled on the same tack and approaching an obstruction to leeward. Can the leeward yacht hail the windward yacht for room and tack at the same time?
11. If the obstruction above is also a mark of the course, is the leeward yacht entitled to room?
12. Is a right of way boat under any obligation to avoid a collision?
13. Which flag is hoisted to register a protest in a race?
14. If a member of the crew touches a mark accidentally, has the mark been fouled?
15. Can a yacht be disqualified or penalised for not observing a rule requiring her to keep clear, even though no collision has taken place?
16. If a yacht continues in a race, even though a protest has been lodged, can other boats treat her as being disqualified?
17. When a yacht has to keep clear of another, can the right of way yacht obstruct her from doing so?
18. If two yachts tack or gybe at the same time, which one must keep clear?
19. When does a yacht actually finish a race?
20. At what point in a race can a yacht safely ignore the racing rules?

nightwatch

'I can't find the scotch anywhere.'
'I popped it into that little
closet with the round glass
door.'

COLLISION COURSE!

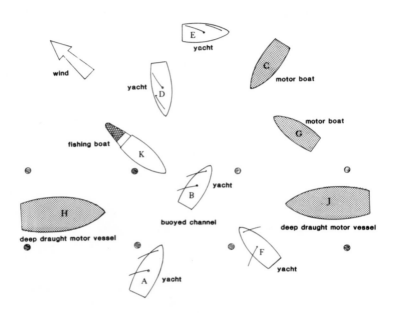

In the diagram above, several boats are navigating through and across a buoyed channel. If the following pairs of boats are at risk of collision, which boat is required to give way and why?

1. A and B ....
2. A and F ....
3. C and B ....
4. D and A ....
5. A and H ....
6. E and B ....
7. G and C ....
8. H and J ....
9. F and K ....
10. K and J ....

SEATALK 2

More seafaring expressions for you to translate:

1. To beat ....
2. To belay ....
3. To broach to ....
4. To check ....
5. To feather ....
6. To flake ....
7. To furl ....
8. To go about ....

9. To gybe ....
10. To heave to ....
11. To luff up ....
12. To reef ....
13. To seize ....
14. To sheet home ....
15. To take in ....

BOOKWORM

Can you link up the ships' names with the books in which they were featured?

1. Treasure Island
2. Gulliver's Travels
3. 20,000 Leagues Under the Sea
4. Kidnapped
5. Riddle of the Sands
6. Capt. Hornblower RN
7. Lord Jim
8. Steaming to Bamboola
9. The Cruel Sea
10. Moby Dick

(a) *Columbianna*
(b) *Pequod*
(c) *Compass Rose*
(d) *Patna*
(e) *Hispaniola*
(f) *Antelope*
(g) *Nautilus*
(h) *Dulcibella*
(i) *Covenant*
(j) *Hotspur*

THREEFOLD PURCHASE

Although the threefold purchase is not often seen on small sailing craft, it can often be found around boatyards and on larger sailing ships such as Thames barges, where its extra power is invaluable. Reeving a threefold purchase appears a tricky job, but if the blocks are placed correctly, it is much easier than it looks. Have a go at working it out on the sketch here. It may help if you imagine what the blocks look like viewed from above. Reeve the fall of the rope through the middle sheave of the upper block to start with ...

SEAFARERS

Here are the names of some men and women who have made their mark on the pages of nautical history. Can you identify their achievements and/ or the names of their ships?

1. Sir Francis Chichester ....
2. Thor Heyerdahl ....
3. Admiral William Bligh ....
4. Capt. Hans Langsdorff ....
5. Naomi James DBE ....
6. Joshua Slocum ....
7. John Paul Jones ....
8. Capt. Fogarty Fegen VC ....
9. Sir Ernest Shackleton ....
10. Gladys Gradley ....

THINGUMIJIG

1. Would a *cranse iron* be found
   (a) at the foot of the shrouds?
   (b) at the top of the mast?
   (c) at the end of a bowsprit?
   (d) attached to the rudder?

2. Would a *claw ring* fit over
   (a) a tiller?
   (b) a boom?
   (c) a mast?
   (d) an anchor?

3. A *handybilly* is
   (a) a portable water tank
   (b) an anchor light
   (c) a hand hook
   (d) a small tackle

4. A *highfield lever* is used to
   (a) adjust tension on a back-stay
   (b) tighten up a topping lift
   (c) release the anchor in an emergency
   (d) release a jammed winch

5. A *gudgeon*
   (a) secures the dinghy oars
   (b) supports the rudder
   (c) pivots a centreboard
   (d) supports the compass

6. A *thimble* is used
   (a) to strengthen a wire or rope eye splice
   (b) to protect thumbs in sail-making
   (c) to plug up small leaks
   (d) to cap the top of the mast

7. A *becket* would be used
   (a) to repair a broken hal-yard
   (b) to drill holes in GRP material
   (c) to secure a sheave inside a block
   (d) to lash the tiller or steer-ing wheel

8. A *trapeze* is used
   (a) to rescue someone fallen overboard
   (b) to pull a water skier
   (c) to climb up a mast
   (d) to stabilise a racing dinghy

9. A *bulkhead* is what land-lubbers call
   (a) a wall
   (b) a ceiling
   (c) a toilet
   (d) a cupboard

10. A *topping lift* is used
    (a) to raise and lower the mast
    (b) to raise the mainsail
    (c) to support a spar or the boom
    (d) to lift the centreboard

11. Viewed in cross-section, the sharp end of a *sailmaker's needle*
    (a) has three sides
    (b) has four sides
    (c) is circular
    (d) is diamond shaped

12. *Irish pendants* suggest that the yacht's owner
    (a) hails from Eire
    (b) belongs to an Irish sailing club
    (c) is visiting Irish waters
    (d) cares little for the boat's appearance

13. *Parrel trucks or beads* may be found
    (a) attached to fishing nets
    (b) decorating a figurehead
    (c) encircling the mast
    (d) marking a lead line for gauging depths

14. If a boat has a *taffrail* it will be found
    (a) near the bows
    (b) either side of the wheelhouse
    (c) leading into the cabin
    (d) around the stern

15. A *doghouse* is
    (a) a raised, covered-in extension to a cabin
    (b) a bunk that is mainly enclosed
    (c) a place for keeping animals aboard ship
    (d) a locker for stowing general junk

16. A *clinometer* measures
    (a) the quality of the fresh water
    (b) the angle of heel
    (c) the humidity of the atmosphere
    (d) the speed of the wind

17. *Oakum* is used
    (a) to seal seams between deck planking
    (b) to construct wooden keels
    (c) to repair leaking seacocks
    (d) to clean dirty sails

18. A *bobstay* is attached between
    (a) a bowsprit and the stem
    (b) a gaff and the mast
    (c) a stanchion (support post) and the deck
    (d) a leeboard and the side of a barge

19. A *pelorus* measures
    (a) tension in steel wire
    (b) horizontal angles
    (c) the depth of the sea bed
    (d) vertical angles

20. A *thwart* is
    (a) a stout wooden peg
    (b) a stopper knot
    (c) a small iron ring
    (d) a seat across a dinghy

WEATHER LORE

Many simple rhymes exist to help the sailor forecast the weather. Some are quite useful, but others are quite unreliable. From the small selection below, can you say which ones are to be relied upon?

1. If St Swithins weeps, the proverb says,
   The weather will be foul for forty days.

2. If woolly fleece deck the heavenly way,
   Be sure no rain will mar a summer's day.

3. When mist takes to the open sea,
   Fine weather, shipmate, it will be.

4. March, month as black as a ram
   Comes in like lion, goes out like lamb.

5. When round the moon there is a brough,
   The weather comes in cold and rough.

6. When rise commences after low,
   Squalls expect and then clear blow.

7. Red sky at night, sailor's delight,
   Red sky at morning, sailor take warning.

8. Long foretold, long past,
   Short notice, soon past.

9. When the wind follows the sun
   Fine weather will ne'er be done.

10. Birds and beasts show signs of fear
    And cats don't sleep when a storm is near.

nightwatch

'Well, they laughed at Panama, but he went right ahead and dug his canal.'

LIGHT UP

1. The following vessels are required to show red and green sidelights:
   (a) yachts under 7 m in length   TRUE/FALSE
   (b) yachts over 7 m in length   TRUE/FALSE
   (c) power driven vessels   TRUE/FALSE
   (d) vessels at anchor   TRUE/FALSE
   (e) vessels aground   TRUE/FALSE
   (f) fishing boats   TRUE/FALSE
   (g) vessels engaged in towing   TRUE/FALSE
   (h) vessels not under command but still
       making way   TRUE/FALSE

2. In terms of displayed lights, what is the link between a ship at anchor and a small (under 7 m) yacht under way?

3. Vessels required to show sidelights are also required to show a stern light (or its equivalent).   TRUE/FALSE

4. Fishing vessels are required to show an all-round red or green light above an all-round white light. Which colour is displayed by
   (a) trawlers?
   (b) fishing boats other than trawlers?

5. How many navigation lights should a trawler display when it is hauling its nets?
   (a) 3
   (b) 4
   (c) 5
   (d) 7

6. A large power-driven vessel and a vessel towing both show two white masthead lights. How can you tell one vessel from the other?

7. Ships carry two all-round red lights when they are
   (a) aground
   (b) restricted in manoeuvrability
   (c) not under command
   What does (a) have above these lights that (b) has between, and which (c) doesn't show at all?

MEMORY BANK (See page 9)

BOSUN'S LOCKER

1. If binoculars are described as 7 × 50, what do these figures mean?
2. What is the link between a fog locker and a long stand, and who might be looking for them?
3. In France it's called the Bureau Véritas, in Germany, Germanischer Lloyd, and in Japan, Nipon Kozi Ngokai. What is it in Britain?
4. What is the connection between an astrolabe, a backstaff, and a sextant?
5. Who might be found using a head stick, serving board, fid, rubber, and heaving mallet?
6. What's the difference between flotsam and jetsam?
7. In 1842, the sea parachute was invented. Although it never worked, what was it designed to do?
8. In French it's called a gaffe, in Dutch a pikhaak, and in Spanish a bichero. What it's called in English when it slips overboard is usually unprintable. What is it?
9. If fishermen or women went to catch herrings, would they use a trawler or a drifter?
10. Pilot books occasionally describe distances in cables. How long is a cable?

BIRDS OF A FEATHER

Ten common sea and shore birds are hidden in the grid below. The names run in all directions: forwards, backwards, up, down, and diagonally. *Some cross each other.* When you have managed to locate them, place them alongside one of the descriptions provided.

E	S	P	R	N	A	C	T	H	O	Q	R	F
K	I	L	E	Q	I	O	P	O	H	T	U	S
I	L	O	P	E	T	R	E	L	N	I	W	F
T	K	V	O	B	T	M	J	I	A	W	E	O
T	C	E	R	A	Z	O	R	B	I	L	L	S
I	E	R	N	O	D	R	E	P	M	E	R	A
W	M	N	L	R	D	A	O	A	R	O	U	F
A	K	C	N	I	E	N	R	T	Y	Z	C	X
K	R	T	N	A	E	T	S	J	B	E	N	W
E	D	S	A	K	S	E	R	A	M	L	U	F
N	M	L	P	O	K	T	S	E	T	U	P	V

1...................... A gull-shaped white and grey bird that follows ships and nests in colonies.

2...................... A gull-shaped bird with a yellow-green beak that frequents cliffs and rocks.

3...................... A swallow-shaped bird that dives to pick fish neatly from the water.

4...................... A large wader found on mudflats and estuaries. It has a distinctive, sad, whistling call.

5...................... A hawk-shaped bird that hovers in search of prey.

6...................... A small-beaked bird often found on mud flats. An expert at camouflaging its eggs.

7...................... An odd-shaped bird that jumps up before diving into water.

8 . . . . A small sooty black bird that skims and
paddles across water.
9 . . . . A large bird notable for its spectacular
dives to catch fish, which it eats under-
water.
10 . . . . An ocean bird and a regular victim of oil
pollution.

PART 3   Force 8 to 10 Gale to storm

HEAD IN THE CLOUDS

Here is a quiz which may be of some help in learning to identify different
types of clouds. Using the clues provided, see if you can work out the
names of 10 cloud descriptions.

1. A high-level wispy cloud
2. A high-level towering cloud
3. A high-level layered cloud
4. A medium-level towering cloud
5. A medium-level layered cloud
6. A low-level towering cloud
7. A low-level layered cloud
8. A low-level rain-bearing cloud
9. A thick, towering cloud
10. A rain-bearing towering cloud

Clues:

1. Clouds are described according to their *level*.
    High clouds (18,000′–45,000′)   *cirrus* or *cirro-*
    Medium clouds (6,000′–18,000′)   *alto-*
    Low clouds (1,000′–6,000′)   *stratus* or *strato-*

2. Clouds are described according their *type*.
    Towering cloud   *-cumulus* or *cumulo-*
    Flat or layered cloud   *-stratus*

3. Rain-bearing clouds are associated with   *-nimbus* or *nimbo-*
    towering or low clouds

Of course, there are many other kinds of cloud terms, such as fracto-
(broken clouds), castellatus (castle-like), etc., but you have enough here to
get you started.

STRIKE A LIGHT

Lights are provided as an aid to navigation from lighthouses, lightships, beacons and buoys. How well do you know the general principles which govern their use?

1. The *characteristic* of a light is
   (a) its colour
   (b) the way it flashes on and off
   (c) its height above sea-level
   (d) its normal range of visibility
   (e) all of these items

2. On a chart, which two of the following pieces of information are *not* provided for a buoy?
   (a) the height above sea-level
   (b) the normal range of visibility
   (c) the colour
   (d) the way it flashes on and off

3. An *occulting light* is one where
   (a) the period of darkness exceeds the period of light
   (b) the period of light is the same as the period of darkness
   (c) the period of light exceeds the period of darkness
   (d) the light and dark periods vary irregularly

4. A *quick flashing* buoy produces
   (a) 30–49 flashes per minute
   (b) 50–79 flashes per minute
   (c) 80–159 flashes per minute
   (d) 160+ flashes per minute

5. On a chart, the letter F next to a light indicates a
   (a) foul area buoy
   (b) fixed and flashing light
   (c) flashing light
   (d) fixed light

6. The light in a lightvessel is positioned
   (a) 8 metres above sea-level
   (b) 10 metres above sea-level
   (c) 12 metres above sea-level
   (d) 14 metres above sea-level

7. The elevation of a land-based light refers to its height above
   (a) ground
   (b) mean high water (springs)
   (c) mean low water (springs)
   (d) lowest astronomical tide

8. Some lights show different colours over different areas or zones. These are known as
   (a) multicoloured lights
   (b) alternating lights
   (c) sectored lights
   (d) multipurpose lights

9. When the bearing of a light appears on a chart or in a table, this is given as
   (a) a magnetic bearing from the light
   (b) a magnetic bearing from the sea
   (c) a true bearing from the light
   (d) a true bearing from the sea

10. The loom (diffuse glow) of a light which may appear before a light breaks the horizon is
    (a) potentially quite useful to the navigator
    (b) best ignored until the light actually appears
    (c) too rare a phenomenon to be of any practical use
    (d) too distorted to provide any aid to navigation

11. If you saw a powerful blue light flashing and sweeping the horizon from a lighthouse, this would be
    (a) a warning that the lighthouse light was faulty
    (b) an aid to attract the attention of a helicopter
    (c) a warning of gales in the area
    (d) a fog detector light

12. A South cardinal buoy is placed to the South of an obstruction or hazard. What kind of light might it display?
    (a) 3 quick flashes
    (b) 9 quick flashes
    (c) 6 quick flahses + 1 long flash
    (d) a continual flashing light

nightwatch

'Were you in the silent service?'
'No – the inarticulate one.'

CHART SYMBOLS 2

Here is a selection of some temporary chart symbols commonly used by navigators. Your task is to link the right symbol with the right description.

1.   ... (a) Position by a fix

2.   ... (b) Tidal stream

3. or   ... (c) Transferred position line

4.   ... (d) Course made good

5. 80°   ... (e) Position by dead reckoning

6.   ... (f) Estimated position

7.   ... (g) Position line

8.   ... (h) Course steered

9.   ... (i) Transit bearing

10.   ... (j) Clearing line or bearing

RECORD BREAKERS

1. What is usually claimed to be the first sailing race?
2. What is the oldest yacht club in the world?
3. Where is the largest marina in the world?
4. How many boats took place in the largest race ever held?
5. How old is the oldest motor-driven vessel still in operation?
6. How heavy was the largest sailing vessel ever built?
7. What was the largest passenger ship ever built?
8. What was unusual about the barque *Thomas W Lawson* (5,218 tons) that sank in the English Channel in 1907?
9. What is the longest day's run claimed by a sailing ship?

10. The warship HM *Téméraire* ('*The Fighting Téméraire*') had the largest sail wardrobe. How many square feet (or square metres) did it cover?
11. How long was the smallest ship to cross the Atlantic Ocean?
12. What nationality was the first ship to circumnavigate the globe?
13. What was the name of the first British ship to sail around the world?
14. How large is the world's largest cargo ship?
15. What is the current world speed record for a sailing boat?

JUST A LOAD OF WIND

1. Wind blows from a high pressure area to a low pressure area   TRUE/FALSE

2. Wind speed increases with height above sea-level   TRUE/FALSE

3. A sea-to-land wind is deflected more than a land-to-sea wind   TRUE/FALSE

4. In both hemispheres, wind blows in an anti-clockwise direction around an area of low pressure   TRUE/FALSE

5. Wind coming off high ground is more turbulent (variable and gusty) than a surface wind   TRUE/FALSE

6. The closer the isobars on a weather map, the slower the wind   TRUE/FALSE

7. Wind tends to increase in speed around a prominent headland   TRUE/FALSE

8. Wind generally accelerates as it passes from land to sea   TRUE/FALSE

9. In the Beaufort wind scale, a wind speed of 30 knots represents a gale (Force 8)   TRUE/FALSE

10. A gentle breeze is stronger than a light breeze   TRUE/FALSE

SIGNPOSTS

Once there were thirty different buoyage systems in operation around the world. In recent years there has been a great deal of standardisation, though some differences still exist. The chart (or navigator's nightmare) below contains eleven buoys or marks but each one is in the wrong position. With the help of the numbered positions, can you relocate them? You can assume that the harbour is not in North or South America or in Japan. Confused? Don't plan a round-the-world cruise until you've checked out the answers.

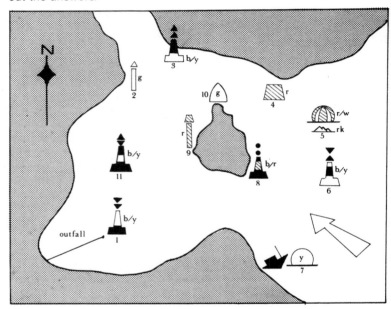

Notes:
The large outline arrow indicates the direction of buoyage.
Colour codes: b/y = black and yellow; r/w = red and white;
b/r = black and red; y = yellow; g = green; r = red.

Use the existing position of each buoy to complete the table.

Position	Correct buoy/mark	Position	Correct buoy/mark
1	___	6	___
2	___	7	___
3	___	8	___
4	___	9	___
5	___	10	___
		11	___

SEATALK 3

1.	To arm	9.	To frap.....................
2.	To bowse....................	10.	To marl ....
3.	To cant.....................	11.	To pinch ....
4.	To careen	12.	To reeve ....
5.	To caulk....................	13.	To scarf....................
6.	To claw off	14.	To swig ....
7.	To clew up	15.	To worm ....
8.	To crowd on.................		

PEA SOUPER

Here are some sounds required to be made by vessels in fog. See if you can link the right sounds with the right vessel.

a) 1 long and 2 short blasts every 2 minutes

b) 1 long and 3 short blasts every 2 minutes

c) 1 long every 2 minutes

d) 2 long every 2 minutes

e) A bell rung rapidly for 5 seconds every minute

f) 3 bell strokes before and after a bell rung rapidly for 5 seconds every minute

1. A power-driven vessel making no way through the water ....
2. A vessel not under command ....
3. A vessel aground ....
4. A fishing vessel ....
5. A vessel towing another ....
6. A sailing vessel ....
7. A vessel restricted in ability to manoeuvre ....
8. A power-driven vessel under way ....
9. A vessel at anchor ....
10. A vessel being towed ....

35

SHAPE UP!

By day, which of the shapes illustrated do these vessels display?

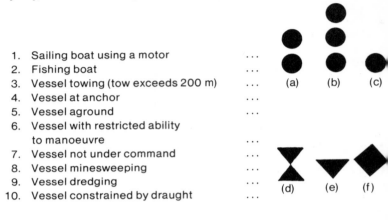

1. Sailing boat using a motor ...
2. Fishing boat ...
3. Vessel towing (tow exceeds 200 m) ...
4. Vessel at anchor ...
5. Vessel aground ...
6. Vessel with restricted ability
   to manoeuvre ...
7. Vessel not under command ...
8. Vessel minesweeping ...
9. Vessel dredging ...
10. Vessel constrained by draught ...

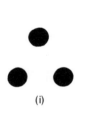

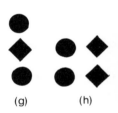

ATLANTIC CROSSING

When an American yachtsman uses the following terms, what are the British equivalents?

1. Hiking stick ....
2. Marconi rig ....
3. Slickers ....
4. Rubrail ....
5. Boom vang ....
6. Heavy air ....
7. Oarlock ....
8. Sail snap ....
9. Jigger ....
10. Gunk holing ....

DO THEY MEAN US?

Here are some more sounds which might be heard from another boat or ship. See if you can identify the correct meaning from the answers provided.

1. One short blast
   - (a) I am altering course to starboard
   - (b) I am going astern
   - (c) Get out of my way
   - (d) Just testing the foghorn

2. Two short blasts
   - (a) You are still in my way
   - (b) I am going astern
   - (c) Hullo sailor!
   - (d) I am altering course to port

3. Three short blasts
   - (a) Keep clear of me
   - (b) I have run aground
   - (c) I am going astern
   - (d) You are on the wrong side of the channel

4. Five short blasts
   - (a) We are having boat drill
   - (b) Fire aboard!
   - (c) I don't understand your intentions
   - (d) I have a dangerous cargo aboard

5. One long blast
   - (a) I'm coming round the bend
   - (b) Turn to or action stations for the crew
   - (c) You can cross ahead of me
   - (d) A traditional farewell to a port

6. Two long and one short
   - (a) I'm overtaking on your starboard side
   - (b) I have a pilot on board
   - (c) I need a pilot
   - (d) I need a doctor

7. Two long and two short blasts
   - (a) No such signal
   - (b) I require medical assistance
   - (c) Man overboard!
   - (d) I am overtaking you to port

8. Four blasts: one long, one short, one long, one short
   - (a) I can offer assistance
   - (b) I agree to be overtaken
   - (c) I don't need your help
   - (d) I don't give a damn

VICTOR HOTEL FOXTROT

1. VHF normally has a range of
   (a) 10–15 miles
   (b) 25–30 miles
   (c) 50–70 miles
   (d) 80–100 miles

2. VHF radio can have a total of
   (a) 15 channels
   (b) 25 channels
   (c) 45 channels
   (d) 55 channels

3. The international distress, safety, and calling frequency is on
   (a) Channel 16
   (b) Channel 6
   (c) Channel 22
   (d) Channel 67

4. The system by which a set can transmit and receive simultaneously (like a telephone) is known as
   (a) simplex
   (b) duplex
   (c) complex
   (d) dual watch

5. Citizens' Band (CB) radio can now be considered as a less-costly substitute for VHF   TRUE/FALSE

6. Radio silence periods last three minutes, starting
   (a) on the hour and half-hour
   (b) before the hour and half-hour
   (c) on the quarter and three-quarter hour
   (d) before the quarter and three-quarter hour

7. All broadcasting is forbidden during the silence periods
                                                      TRUE/FALSE

8. Which of the following signal words – MAYDAY, PAN PAN, SÉCURITÉ – might be used to preface the situations listed?
   (a) to report a navigation hazard (e.g. a buoy out of position)
   (b) to request urgent assistance (e.g. vessel sinking)
   (c) to request assistance in retrieving a man overboard

9. In the following outline of a distress call, an important piece of information has been omitted. What is it? ....
   the MAYDAY signal

name of the vessel
nature of distress
aid required
number of people requiring aid
the OVER procedure

10. Distress, urgency, or safety *signals* should be repeated
    (a) twice
    (b) three times
    (c) four times
    (d) five times

11. Shortened versions of the international figure codes (zero for nadazero, five for pantafive, etc.) are permissible   TRUE/FALSE

12. Which of the following procedural words or phrases are permissible?
    (a) Read back
    (b) I spell
    (c) Over and out
    (d) Roger

13. What is the difference between SEELONCE FEENEE (f. *Silence fini*) and PRUDONCE (f. *Prudence*)?

14. Reporting by VHF to traffic control centres and ports in European waters is governed by standardised regulations   TRUE/FALSE

15. *Seaspeak* is a recommended system of 'marking' the start of a message to clarify its meaning. Which of the following prefixes are recommended?
    (a) a question
    (b) an instruction
    (c) advice
    (d) a request
    (e) information
    (f) a warning
    (g) an intention

TIME AND TIDE

1. Neap tides occur when the sun and moon are opposite each other   TRUE/FALSE

2. Strong winds have little or no effect on the height of the tide   TRUE/FALSE

3. The tide takes longer to flood than to ebb   TRUE/FALSE

4.	Spring tides produce higher low tides than neap tides	TRUE/FALSE
5.	In the Pacific Ocean, tides occur twice as frequently as in the Atlantic Ocean	TRUE/FALSE
6.	Depths of water on a chart are based on the lowest astronomical tide	TRUE/FALSE
7.	Unpredictable and irregular tides are referred to as *mixed tides*	TRUE/FALSE
8.	In any one port, high water at spring tides always occurs at about the same time of day	TRUE/FALSE
9.	Atmospheric pressure can alter the level of a tide by as much as 1 foot	TRUE/FALSE
10.	The greatest rate of change in the height of a tide occurs towards the last hour of the flood or ebb	TRUE/FALSE

CHART SYMBOLS 3

More widely-used chart symbols and abbreviations for you to decipher.

1. . . . .

2. . . . .

3. . . . .

4. . . . .

5. . . . .

6. or . . . .

7. . . . .

8. . . . .

9. . . . .

10. RC . . . .

11. . . . .

(ODAS)

12. Explos . . . .

13. Mo . . . .

14. dir . . . .

15. Dn . . . .

16. P A . . . .

17. Mont . . . .

18. Ldg . . . .

19. cov . . . .

20. Np . . . .

NIGHTMARE

Here is a nautical version of an old riddle. Some people see the solution almost immediately, whereas others puzzle over it for hours – even days.

* * * * * * * * * * * * *

One cold and wet evening an old cargo ship was lurching slowly across the North Atlantic Ocean. The third mate was brewing a cup of tea in the chartroom and the lookout huddled miserably behind the bridge dodger to avoid the rain.

In the radio cabin, the ship's radio officer sat nodding sleepily by his receiver and his head sank lower and lower until it was almost resting on the bench in front of him and he fell asleep. In his dream he imagined he was living in Paris at the time of the Revolution and was on his way to the guillotine, to the jeers of a large and violent crowd. Struggling desperately for his life, he was dragged up the steps to the platform and his neck laid across the fatal plank. Stricken with absolute terror he awaited the falling blade.

At that moment, with the tea brewed, the third mate popped his head around the radio room door. Seeing the operator asleep, he leaned across and tapped him smartly on the back of his neck with a teaspoon. 'Wake up, Sparks – tea's ready,' he called.

The radio operator fell dead at his post!

* * * * * * * * * * * * *

The problem: Although such a fatality is possible, what evidence does the story contain which proves that it cannot have happened?

SEA LAWYER

The Law of the Sea is very much an international affair, decided at United Nations conferences and World conventions. Sometimes there is much disagreement, particularly on items such as exclusion zones and territorial waters, and certain matters take as long as ten years before general agreement is reached.

Here are some basic facts from international sea law; see how many you know.

1. An island is an area of land which is surrounded by water at
   (a) high water
   (b) low water
   (c) mid-tide

2. Territorial seas extend from the coastline for a distance of
   (a) 3 miles
   (b) 10 miles
   (c) 12 miles
   (d) 18 miles

3. In territorial waters, visiting submarines are required to navigate on the surface and show their flag   TRUE/FALSE

4. The high seas are open to all nations for the following activities
   (a) navigation   TRUE/FALSE
   (b) laying of submarine cables and pipelines   TRUE/FALSE
   (c) construction of artificial islands   TRUE/FALSE
   (d) slave trading   TRUE/FALSE
   (e) any kind of fishing   TRUE/FALSE
   (f) scientific research   TRUE/FALSE
   (g) overflight   TRUE/FALSE
   (h) any form of broadcasting   TRUE/FALSE

5. If, for convenience, a ship sails under two national flags, it is treated
   (a) as if it belongs to the larger state
   (b) as if it belongs to the nearer state
   (c) as if it has dual nationality
   (d) as if it is stateless

6. A warship on the high seas is completely free from the jurisdiction of any other country   TRUE/FALSE

7. Though a tradition of the sea, a ship's master has no legal obligation to give assistance to people in distress at sea   TRUE/FALSE

8. A pirate ship automatically loses its original nationality

TRUE/FALSE

9. Only warships and similar vessels can arrest or seize a ship engaged in piracy

TRUE/FALSE

10. If a country believes that a ship has violated its laws, in certain circumstances it may take action to follow and stop that ship. This is known as
    (a) hot pursuit
    (b) marine arrest
    (c) a seizure chase
    (d) maritime apprehension

11. Landlocked countries have no right of access to the sea

TRUE/FALSE

12. No country can claim sovereignty over any part of the high seas

TRUE/FALSE

13. Artificial islands and structures have the same status as real islands

TRUE/FALSE

nightwatch

'He's a responsible member of the crew.
If anything goes wrong he's usually
responsible.'

MICROS AWEIGH!

Although a microcomputer might appear more appropriate for solving deep-sea navigation problems, it can have some very practical uses for those whose sailing is of a more modest nature. Its ability to repeat a sequence of complicated calculations makes it an ideal aid for producing reference tables that are specifically tailored to the needs of the user. It is not necessary, however, to carry one aboard, for there are a number of navigation aids which may be developed at home during the winter lay-up or prior to a sailing trip.

Many computer users find program listings time-consuming and tiring to copy, but the programs presented here are very short and will take only a few minutes to type in on a keyboard. The programs were developed for a BBC Microcomputer but have been rewritten so that they may be transferred to most popular makes of microcomputer with only a few minor adjustments. They require a printer and the appropriate micro-computer instruction for switching it on.

The first program, AZIMUTH, is designed to provide the user with a list of the true bearings (to the nearest degree) of sunset or sunrise for any day of the year from a given latitude. Armed with this table, the navigator may check the hand bearing compass whenever the right opportunity arises. The program requests the latitude (in degrees and decimal places) and then produces a table similar to that illustrated but covering 365 days starting from March 21st. With such a coverage, compass checking can take place throughout the year – even ashore! A table of this kind is a handy guide for those whose cruising grounds are limited to a small range of latitude, but, if necessary, several tables could be printed to cover a wider range. True enthusiasts may like to amend the program for a leap year.

The second program, TIDES, has been developed to produce a table indicating the state of a rising or falling tide at intervals of 15 minutes. The essential data for insertion here are (i) the range of the tide in metres, and (ii) the interval between high and low water in minutes. These are requested by the program each time it is run.

There's nothing much wrong with the popular 'twelfths' rule, but a lot can happen in the middle of the tide and inaccuracies invariably creep in. To obtain full benefit from this program, it will be necessary to develop a small series of tables covering a range of tide heights and intervals depending on local circumstances. The actual height of the tide is obtained by adding the height of low water to the figures printed in the table.

Line 20 of the program is a BBC Micro instruction to print figures to two decimal places. Other micros may require a different instruction and handbooks should be consulted.

The third program, MORSE, has been designed as an aid to learning morse code. The program offers three speed options and allows the user to include or exclude sound. Letters are generated randomly and the morse code sequence is flashed on the screen (with or without sound). After each coded item, the letter will be revealed on the screen when the RETURN key is pressed. A second press of the RETURN key produces the next coded letter, and so on.

Lines specific to the BBC Micro are as follows:

180   alters the screen 'mode' to enlarge the flashing morse light
240   clears the flashing cursor from the screen
270   sound for dots
330   sound for dashes

The program will work without these lines, but will not produce the sound of the morse code.

Readers who lack a home computer should not be discouraged. Many local schools now have this facility, plus a computer club whose members are usually eager to copy and try out small programs – particularly those which have some educational value. Microcomputers will also become more widely available through local or college libraries. But beware! Like sailing, computing can become very addictive and a 'regular fix' may take on an entirely different meaning.

AZIMUTH

```
     >LIST
 10 REM AZIMUTH PROGRAM
 20 DIM D(13),M(13),R(13)
 30 PRINT
 40 INPUT"Latitude",L
 50 INPUT"N or S",H$
 60 FOR C=1 TO 13:READ D(C):READ M(C):READ R(C):NEXT
 70 PRINT
 80 PRINT"Date      Sunrise  Sunset"
 90 PRINT
100 FOR S= 0 TO 360 STEP .98630137
110 K=23.4467*(SIN(RAD(S)))
120 DAY=DAY +1
130 GOSUB 200
140 A=DEG(ASN(1/COS(RAD(L))*(SIN(RAD(K))))))
150 IF H$="N" THEN D=270+A
160 IF H$="S" THEN D=270-A
170 PRINT;M;" ";DY;TAB(12)INT(360.5-D);TAB(20);INT(D)
180 NEXT S
190 END
200 FOR C= 1 TO 13
210 IF DAY<D(C) THEN M=M(C):DY=DAY-R(C):GOTO230
220 NEXT
230 RETURN
240 DATA 12,3,-20,42,4,11
250 DATA 73,5,41,103,6,72
260 DATA 134,7,102,165,8,133
270 DATA 195,9,164,226,10,194
280 DATA 256,11,225,287,12,255
290 DATA 318,1,286,346,2,317
300 DATA 366,3,345
```

>RUN

```
Latitude?51.8
N or S?N

Date       Sunrise  Sunset

3 21         90       270
3 22         89       270
3 23         89       271
3 24         88       271       sample run
3 25         87       272
3 26         87       273
3 27         86       273
3 28         85       274
3 29         85       275
3 30         84       275
3 31         83       276
4  1         83       277
4  2         82       277
```

46

TIDES

```
>LIST
   10 REM TIDE PROGRAM
   20 @%=131594
   30 INPUT"Range",R
   40 INPUT"Interval",I
   50 PRINT:PRINT
   60 PRINT"TIDE TABLE"
   70 PRINT
   80 PRINT"                EBB              FLOOD"
   90 PRINT"Time            mtrs    feet     mtrs    feet"
  100 PRINT
  110 FOR K= 0 TO I STEP 15
  120 A=(K*180)/I
  130 C=R*SIN(RAD(A/2))*SIN(RAD(A/2))
  140 T=K/60
  150 M=.6*(T-INT(T))
  160 PRINT; INT(T)+M;TAB(11)R-C;TAB(18)(R-C)*3.28;
  165 PRINT;TAB(26)C;TAB(33)C*3.28
  170 NEXT
  180 END
```

```
>RUN
Range?4.5
Interval?300
```

TIDE TABLE				
	EBB		FLOOD	
Time	mtrs	feet	mtrs	feet
0.00	4.50	14.76	0.00	0.00
0.15	4.47	14.67	0.03	0.09
0.30	4.39	14.40	0.11	0.36
0.45	4.25	13.96	0.25	0.80
1.00	4.07	13.35	0.43	1.41
1.15	3.84	12.60	0.66	2.16
1.30	3.57	11.72	0.93	3.04
1.45	3.27	10.73	1.23	4.03
2.00	2.95	9.66	1.55	5.10
2.15	2.60	8.53	1.90	6.23
2.30	2.25	7.38	2.25	7.38
2.45	1.90	6.23	2.60	8.53
3.00	1.55	5.10	2.95	9.66
3.15	1.23	4.03	3.27	10.73
3.30	0.93	3.04	3.57	11.72
3.45	0.66	2.16	3.84	12.60
4.00	0.43	1.41	4.07	13.35
4.15	0.25	0.80	4.25	13.96
4.30	0.11	0.36	4.39	14.40
4.45	0.03	0.09	4.47	14.67
5.00	0.00	0.00	4.50	14.76

sample run

MORSE

```
>LIST
   10 REM MORSE TRAINING PROGRAM
   20 DIM M$(26),N$(26)
   30 CLS
   40 PRINT
   50 PRINT"Type 1 for SLOW"
   60 PRINT"Type 2 for MEDIUM"
   70 PRINT"Type 3 for FAST"
   80 PRINT
   90 INPUT SP
  100 PRINT
  110 PRINT "Type S for sound or any key for silence"
  120 PRINT
  130 INPUT S$
  140 ON SP GOSUB 440,460,480
  150 FOR K=1 TO 26
  160 READ M$(K),N$(K)
  170 NEXT K
  180 MODE5
  190 FOR S= 1 TO 2000:NEXT
  200 K=RND(26)
  210 J=1
  220 FOR L= 1 TO LEN (M$(K))
  230 PRINTTAB(8,13);"*"
  240 VDU 23,1,0;0;0;0;
  250 IF MID$(M$(K),L,1)= "1" THEN 320
  260 IF S$<>"S" THEN 280
  270 SOUND 1,-10,120,A/80
  280 FOR S = 1 TO A:NEXT S
  290 CLS
  300 FOR S = 1 TO C:NEXT S
  310 GOTO 370
  320 IF S$<>"S" THEN 340
  330 SOUND 1,-10,120,B/80
  340 FOR S=1 TO B:NEXT S
  350 CLS
  360 FOR S = 1 TO C:NEXT S
  370 NEXT L
  380 X = GET
  390 PRINT TAB(8,13);N$(K)
  400 PRINTTAB(0,0);
  410 X=GET
  420 CLS
  430 GOTO 190
  440 LET A = 2000:LET B=500:LET C=400
  450 RETURN
  460 LET A=1000:LET B=250:LET C=200
  470 RETURN
  480 LET A=500:LET B=125:LET C=100
  490 RETURN
  500 DATA 12,A,2111,B,2121,C,211,D,1,E,1121,F,221,G
  510 DATA 1111,H,11,I,1222,J,212,K,1211,L,22,M,21,N
  520 DATA 222,O,1221,P,2212,Q,121,R,111,S,2,T,112,U
  530 DATA 1112,V,122,W,2112,X,2122,Y,2211,Z
```

48

ANSWERS PART 1

SAILING (p.2)

1. Close-hauled, reaching, and running.
2. (a) In stays or in irons – the latter is used when the boat stops head to wind, unable to pay off either way (b) Close reaching (c) Broad reaching (d) On a dead run (e) Sailing by the lee (but watch out for an accidental gybe)
3. (a) Ready about! (b) Ready to gybe!
4. (a) Lee-Oh! (b) Gybe-Oh!
5. (a) Luff!, or Luff up! (b) Check!, or Steady!, or Steady as she goes! (c) Bear away!

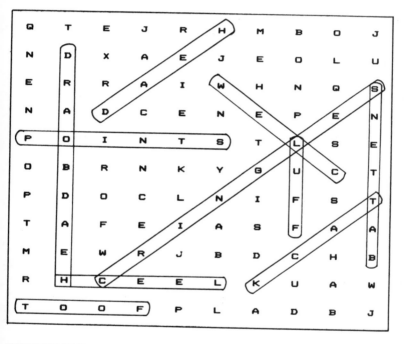

WORDSEARCH (p. 3)

1. headboard 2. luff 3. points 4. tack 5. foot
6. battens 7. clew 8. cringles 9. leech 10. head

SEATALK 1 (p. 4)

1. To close openings from the sea or weather
2. To push away
3. To start moving
4. To lean over
5. To struggle and make little headway
6. To move a boat into water
7. To record information; to achieve a distance
8. To secure or tie up
9. To set sails and gather speed
10. To let out line or rope gradually
11. To propel using one oar
12. To maintain course and speed
13. To pack things away
14. To remove or lift out
15. To lift (as in 'weigh the anchor')

DIFFERENCES 1 (p. 4)

1. There is no universally accepted definition for these terms, but among the various definitions for boats are the following: non-ocean going, a small open craft, propelled by oars, having no accommodation, carries six or less passengers (US), capable of being carried by a ship. Definitions for a ship include having three masts (if a sailing ship), containing accommodation, sea-going, over 100 feet in length, carrying more than six passengers (US).

2. A sloop is a single-masted sailing boat setting a mainsail and one headsail. A cutter is similar but sets more than one headsail.

3. Both are two-masted boats with fore and aft sails, but the mizzen mast of a yawl is stepped abaft the rudder.

4. A brig is a two-masted sailing ship square-rigged on both masts. A brigantine is similar but square-rigged only on the foremast.

5. A barque is a three-masted sailing ship with the two forward masts square-rigged. A barquentine is similar but is square-rigged only on the foremast.

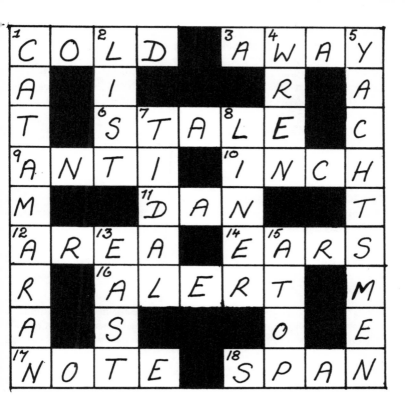

QUICK CROSSWORD (p. 5)

CAPSIZE (p. 6)

Circumstances under which capsizes occur can vary, but in the situation described here, the following steps are the best ones.

1. 13	3. 16	5. 10	7. 4
2. 19	4. 3	6. 9	8. 6

Never undertake 5, 11, 15, or 18.

17 might make things even worse by completely inverting your craft.

1 and 8 shouldn't be necessary, but might be attempted at a late stage in the process if you are having difficulty in righting the boat.

12 will almost certainly be ignored.

14 will leave you with a damaged boat.

2 is a last resort when in grave danger.

CHART SYMBOLS 1 (p. 7)

1. Sand   2. Mud   3. Shingle   4. Pebbles   5. Weed   6. Wreck   7. Beaco
8. Lifeboat station   9. Rock   10. Tower   11. Nautical mile(s)   12. Lc
water 13. Coastguard Station   14. Church or Chapel   15. Visible
16. Notice board   17. Obscured   18. Fort   19. House   20. Lock

RIGHT WAY, WRONG WAY 1 (p. 7)

1. (a) produces more friction to take the strain than (b).
2. (b) is less likely to jam when letting go.

PERSONALITY (p. 8 and p. 9)

Well, are you a loner, an attention-seeker, a leader, a mixer, or a mixture
these descriptions?

Loner: Definitely a single-handed cruising man or woman. Tolerates ra
ing but will probably fail to round the second buoy and will disappear ov
the horizon. Occasionally found nursing a bottle of gin in the peace a
quiet of a remote creek.

Attention-seeker: A boon to the sailing club's entertainment committe
Only enjoys racing if there's a chance of winning or capsizing. Can be a t
of a nuisance on a cruiser, and if a non-swimmer, must always be tethere
by a harness.

Leader: Admires Nelson, Hornblower, Queeg, and Bligh. Usually hea
shouting angrily at wife entering or leaving locks. Regularly seen pointir
derisively from the committee boat.

Mixer: A good guy invariably found ordering (and paying for) drinks, catc
ing heaving lines, pushing open lock gates, etc. Good cruising companic
and genuinely prefers the 'hot bunk system'.

MEMORY BANK (p. 9)

Burgee, eye bolt, bucket, lifebuoy, paintbrush, boat hook, Danforth anch
fender, shackle, knife, log rotator, lamp, dividers, safety harness, de
scrubber.

10 items is an above-average score. Items are often best remembered I
being combined in some way, e.g. the bucket with the deck scrubber. Th
combination, however, need not be a logical one.

A CUTE ANGLE (p. 9)

The answer lies in the first line – a hand. Held at arm's length, a closed fist viewed from the eye subtends an angle of around 10°; extend the thumb and the angle increases to 15°. A wide open hand can encompass an angle of approximately 20° and the width of one finger covers approximately 2°. Such measurements will, of course, vary from one person's hand to another's, but with the aid of a compass or sextant you can check your own 'hand measurements'.

KNOTTY PROBLEM (p. 10)

1. (e) Sheet bend
2. (i) Clove hitch: needs watching, because it can slip if the weight is taken off it.
3. (b) Overhand knot: these tend to appear in ropes just when you don't need them!
4. (a) Carrick bend
5. (d) Figure of eight knot: better than the overhand knot as a stopper knot.
6. (f) Round turn and two half hitches
7. (h) Reef knot
8. (c) Rolling hitch: a good general purpose hitch.
9. (g) Bowline: good general purpose knot for making a bight (loop) in the end of a rope.
10. A knot usually refers to a rope tied to itself in some way; a bend is where one rope is tied to another; a hitch is where a rope is tied around or through another object.

FLAG DAY (p. 11)

No good looking here – keep hunting for a reference book and complete the exercise. Some alternatives to Item 6 'I require assistance' include flames (which could be risky), a square flag with a ball-shape above or below it, continuous sounding of a fog horn or whistle, raising and lowering outstretched arms, dye markers in the sea. Note that the coded signals NC or SOS mean 'I am in distress and require immediate assistance'. The signal W is used when medical assistance is required.

STARGAZER (p. 12)

1. Cassiopaeia (h). Another useful pointer to the Pole Star.
2. Gemini (e): Castor and Pollux – the heavenly twins.
3. Crucis (or Crux) (d). The Southern Cross.
4. Lyra (g). Used to locate Vega.
5. Leo (b). Used to locate Regulus.
6. Taurus (i). Close to the Pleiades or Seven Sisters.
7. Orion (a). The belt of stars in the centre point down to Sirius, the brightest star in the heavens. With skilful location, this star is capable of being seen in daylight.
8. Pegasus (f). A very distinctive square of stars.
9. Cygnus (c). For Beta Cygni – a double star.

SURVIVAL (p. 13)

1. (b), and then cover lightly with a dry dressing. Forget about grease and bursting blisters.
2. (c)
3. (d) and then (c). Seek medical assistance if you are certain that the heart has stopped beating and you are unable to give cardiac massage.
4. (a), the others will cause damage to the skin.
5. (b), through mouth-to-mouth resuscitation.

How well could *you* cope in an emergency? Invest in a good first aid book or, better still, attend a local course.

HELP WANTED (p. 13)

Sir Ernest Shackleton (1874–1922)

DEDUCTION (p. 14)

The race started at 3.10 p.m.

OPPOSITES (p. 14)

1. Starboard: Port
2. Deck: Deckhead (ceiling)
3. Stem: Stern
4. Let go!: Make fast
5. Head (of a sail): Foot
6. Luff (of a sail): Leech
7. Greenwich Meridian: International Date Line (almost)
8. Leeward: Windward
9. ENE: WSW

10.   Astern: Ahead
11.   Tack: To gybe, or the peak of a gaff sail
12.   Abaft: Before or afore
13.   4 points (or broad) on port bow: Broad on the starboard quarter
14.   Forestay: Backstay
15.   Dead run: In irons or in stays
16.   Crown (of anchor): Head
17.   Crown (of block): Arse (believe it or not!) or tail
18.   Pulpit: Pushpit (rails around the stern)
19.   Wake: Bone (foam from the bow wave – 'having a bone in its teeth' is an old seafaring expression)
20.   Bowsprit: Bumpkin or bumkin (a spar projecting aft to which a backstay may be attached)
21.   'At the dip': 'Close up' (refers to position of a flag)
22.   Hogging: Sagging (hogging occurs when a boat bends upwards amidships – sagging is the reverse)
23.   Fore and aft: Athwartships
24.   Head (of a flag): Fly
25.   Boom: Gaff or yard

RIGHT WAY, WRONG WAY 2 (p. 14)

1.   (a) is less likely to jam when letting go
2.   (b) means both lines can be let go with little difficulty. By Sodde's Law, however, a third line will have been thrown over the other two by the time you get back from the bar.

ANSWERS PART 2

NOAH'S ARK (p. 15)

1.   Bulldog grip – a U-shaped clamp.
2.   Bull's eye – a sheave-less pulley or a fairlead; a patch of blue sky at the centre of a revolving storm.
3.   Butterfly block – a small snatch block with a long rope tail.
4.   Cat boat – an unstayed single masted vessel; cat davit – an aid for lifting the anchor clear of the water; cat head – an anchor support projecting from the bows; catspaw – two loops of rope securing a hook.
5.   Cockpit – the centre of operations on a small boat; seacock – an inlet/outlet valve in the ship's hull.
6.   Cow hitch – a simple slip knot for gripping spars.
7.   Crow's nest – a lookout platform attached to a mast.

8. Dog vane – another name for a tell-tale ribbon on the shrouds; dog watch – two 2-hour watches between 4 p.m. and 8 p.m.

9. Duckboards – slatted timber deck boards.

10. Goosewing – to sail with headsail and mainsail on opposite sides; gooseneck – the connection between boom and mast.

11. Horse – a bar supporting the lower block of the mainsheet tackle; also the rope which supports crew working on the yards of a square-rigged vessel.

12. Hounds – that part of a mast where the diameter changes to take the crosstrees; houndsband – a collar around the upper part of a mast.

13. Jackass rig – an unusual combination of masts and/or sails.

14. Monkey island – an enclosed navigation position above the bridge of a ship; monkey's fist – a knot at the throwing end of a heaving line.

15. Mule sail – a staysail hanked upside down between the main and mizzen masts of a ketch for additional power.

16. Otter boards – boards towed to keep trawl nets open.

17. Pelican hook – a quick-release hinged hook.

18. Ram bow – a bow which rakes (slopes) backwards.

19. Ratcatcher – a circular metal guard to prevent rats climbing aboard; ratlines – footropes across the shrouds.

20. Swallow – the upper opening in a block through which the rope passes.

DROPPING THE PICK (p. 15)

1. This prevents the cable from piling up on the anchor and possibly fouling it.

2. Between three and five times the depth of water. Three if using chain, but up to five if using rope and chain. In rough weather you might veer up to ten times the depth.

3. A kedge anchor. As a second anchor, it is used to restrain the boat from swinging around. It can also be used to 'kedge off' – this means laying out the anchor and pulling on it to move the vessel clear.

4. A tripping line is a light line attached to the crown of an anchor. It is used to help free the anchor should it become fouled on the sea bed. The line is usually twice the depth of water.

5. Anchor unsuitable for the ground or seabed, insufficient length of chain/warp, anchor fouled by other tackle, anchor too small or light, change of tide/wind causes anchor to trip itself, seabed sloping steeply.

6. Take bearings on nearby object, transit bearing (two objects in line), check on position relative to nearby boats (hopefully not dragging

their anchors!), listen for rumbling of anchor (not the chain) dragging across seabed, with accompanying vibrations.

7. A fisherman's bend. This is very similar to the round turn and two half hitches on p. 10, but the first hitch passes *through* the two round turns.

8. By day, a black ball-shape. By night, an all-round white riding light.

9. This is a weight shackled over and lowered down the anchor chain. It helps to stop a yacht from snubbing or jerking at her anchor.

10. (a) Get upwind of the mooring or anchorage, drop the mainsail, and sail downwind under headsail alone. Luff up to the mooring or anchorage and let fly the sheet.
(b) Approach under main and headsails across the wind. Gradually turn towards the buoy or anchorage and harden the sheets. Luff up, free the sheets, and moor or anchor.

HARD TACK (P. 16)

(a) *Sea Slug* has the advantage by starting off on the tack which is more directly towards the destination. Almost any change of wind direction will be of greater advantage to *Sea Slug* than to *Ocean Snail*.

INITIALS (p. 16)

1. Steamship   2. Motor vessel   3. Royal Mail Ship   4. Gas Turbine Ship
5. Ore/Bulk/Oil   6. Roll on – Roll off   7. Very Large Crude Carrier
8. Liquified Natural Gas Container   9. Air-Cushioned Vehicle (e.g. hover-craft)   10. Used to define a 'general cargo or container carrier'

SEA JOBS (p. 17)

1. Radio officer   2. Captain   3. Crew's messman (usually a junior seaman)   4. Electrician   5. Donkeyman – senior engineroom rating   6. In a watchkeeping team of three, the one resting from steering or lookout is called the 'farmer'.   7. Lamptrimmer – obsolete now, but occasionally used to describe the bosun's right-hand man or mate.   8. Ship's carpenter   9. Deck officer apprentice or cadet – comes from the naval term 'midshipman'.   10. Captain's personal steward

NAVIGATION (p. 18)

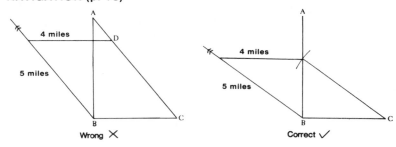

Wrong ✕   Correct ✓

Let A = the anchorage 5 miles away, B = the boat, and C = the 4 knot current.

Some people solve this problem by drawing a line from C to A and take this as the direction of the course to be steered. If, however, this course is transferred to point B, one hour's run (5 miles), and one hour's current (4 miles) will bring the boat to point D – well off course for the anchorage A.

The correct solution is to draw a line representing one hour's sailing (5 miles) from C to where it cuts line AB. This is the direction which the boat should take. With this course transferred to point B, one hour's run (5 miles) and one hour's current (4 miles) will keep the boat on course for point A, the anchorage.

DIFFERENCES 2 (p. 18)

1. The term fog is generally used where visibility is less than 1,000 metres, whereas mist usually indicates visibility between 1 and 2 kilometres.

2. In hawser-laid rope, three strands are laid up right-handed. A cable-laid rope consists of three hawser-laid ropes laid up left-handed – nine strands in all.

3. Both are good mud anchors but the CQR has a swivelling plough-shaped fluke, and the Danforth has two flat flukes which enable it to be stored in a hawsepipe.

4. Technically, in a reef knot the bight of each rope lies over or under both parts of the other. The granny knot looks like a reef knot but is incorrectly made and can result in a knot that slips or jams.

5. A wind is said to back when the direction from which it comes shifts in an anti-clockwise direction. Veering occurs when it shifts in a clockwise direction.

6. The fall is used for hauling on, whereas the standing part does not move.

7. A nautical mile is 1,852 metres or 6,076 ft. A land mile is 1,609 metres or 5,280 ft.

8. When a rope is wrapped in material for protection (parcelling), it is usually served or bound with marline to hold the parcelling in position. In whipping, twine is bound around the end of a rope to prevent the strands from unlaying.
9. A shipbroker helps to negotiate business for a shipowner, whereas a ship chandler supplies ships with stores and provisions.
10. They are the same item – a light pole used to hold the jib out when running.

BASIC RACING QUIZ (p. 19)

1. 10 minutes
2. Usually the International Code Flag P (Blue Peter) as a preparatory signal.
3. It helps to countdown from the ten-minute warning signal. Boats positioned some way from the shore or committee boat may not hear the starting signal until well after it has been made. Accurate timing can save valuable seconds.
4. They are recalled by two guns.
5. When any part of her hull, crew, or equipment crosses the starting line in the direction of the first mark.
6. Starboard tack
7. Square
8. Two lengths
9. If boat A overlaps boat B and boat B overlaps boat C, then boat A overlaps boat C.
10. No
11. Not if the windward yacht can fetch (reach) the mark without tacking.
12. Yes. If no reasonable attempt is made to do so, she may be disqualified.
13. The International Code Flag B, or whatever the club's sailing instructions require.
14. Yes
15. Yes
16. No. She may be exonerated of any blame.
17. No. The right of way yacht must not alter course while the other boat is trying to keep clear.
18. The one on the other's port side.
19. When any part of her hull, crew, or equipment in normal position crosses the finishing line from the direction of the last turn or mark.
20. Assuming the race has not been abandoned, she remains under the rules until she has cleared the finishing line.

COLLISION COURSE! (p. 20)

1. If A is overtaking she must keep clear (Rule 13)
2. F. Windward vessel (Rule 12)
3. C. Motor gives way to sail (Rule 18)
4. D. Port tack gives way to starboard tack (Rule 12)
5. A. H is assumed to be constrained by her draught and has restricted manoeuvrability (Rule 18)
6. B. Both on same tack but B is to windward (Rule 12)
7. G. G has the other motor vessel on her own starboard side (Rule 15)
8. Both H and J should alter course slightly to starboard and proceed down the starboard side of the channel (Rules 9 and 14)
9. F. The fishing vessel or trawler has right of way (Rule 18)
10. K. The fishing vessel does not have right of way over a vessel with restricted manoeuvrability (Rule 9)

SEATALK 2 (p. 21)

1. To sail close-hauled to the wind
2. To secure something (e.g. a line) or to stop or cancel an activity
3. To come round broadside on to the sea
4. To ease out gradually and carefully; to keep rope under tension
5. To turn the blade of an oar parallel to the water
6. To lay out – loosely in folds as with a sail on the boom, or in figures of eight as with rope on the deck. The word 'fake' may also be used.
7. To roll up or gather in
8. To change tack by turning the bows through the wind
9. To change tack by turning the stern through the wind
10. To stop the boat and let her lie head off the wind under the control of the sails or the engine
11. To point a boat's bows closer to the direction of the wind
12. To shorten or reduce the amount of sail
13. To bind two ropes together
14. To pull in the sheets and sails
15. To haul in or lower (e.g. sails)

BOOKWORM (p. 21)

1. (e)   2. (f)   3. (g)   4. (i)   5. (h)   6. (j)   7. (d)   8. (a)   9. (c)   10. (b)

THREEFOLD PURCHASE (p. 22)

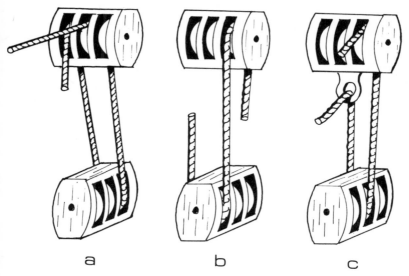

a   b   c

The secret is in the way the blocks are placed one above the other. The sheaves in one face fore and aft, and in the other athwartships. As the rope leaves the top block it leads naturally to the correct sheave in the lower block. From the lower block it leads up to the correct sheave in the upper block, and so on.

SEAFARERS (p. 22)

1. In 1961 he sailed *Gypsy Moth IV* single-handed around the world. He established distance and speed records for solo navigation and revived interest in marine circumnavigation.

2. In 1947, this Norwegian with five companions sailed the balsa wood craft *Kon-Tiki* from Peru to Polynesia to verify a theory of primitive migration.

3. In 1789, as the captain of HMS *Bounty*, was cast adrift in an open boat by mutineers. Reached land after 46 days, along with 18 survivors.

4. In 1939, as commander of the German pocket battleship *Graf Spee*, he scuttled his ship off Montevideo following a fierce engagement with the British Navy.

5. In 1978/79, in the Bermudan sloop *Express Crusader*, she became the first woman to sail around the world via Cape Horn.

6. In 1895/98, in the gaff yawl *Spray*, he became the first man to sail single-handed around the world.

7. This Scots-born seafarer spent the early part of his career as a mate on a

slave trader. In 1778, as a naval officer in the American continental navy, he harried English ports and shipping from the frigate *Ranger* and captured two British warships. He eventually became a rear-admiral in the Russian navy. He was not a member of the RYA.

8. In 1940, his armed merchant cruiser *Jervis Bay* engaged the German battleship *Admiral Scheer*, enabling the majority of ships in a convoy to escape to safety.

9. In 1916, following the abandonment in the Antarctic of the expeditionary ship *Discovery*, he undertook, with members of the crew, an 800-mile journey in a 20' whaler, the *James Caird*, a feat which led to the eventual rescue of every member of the expedition.

10. In 1902, sailing an 18' lugger from Nova Scotia to Devon, she became the first woman to cross the Atlantic single-handed. This feat took her 60 days.

THINGUMIJIG (pp. 23 and 24)

1. (c)   2. (b)   3. (d)   4. (a)   5. (b)   6. (a)   7. (d)   8. (d)   9. (a)   10. (c)
11. (a)   12. (d)   13. (c)   14. (d)   15. (a)   16. (b)   17. (a)   18. (a)
19. (b)   20. (d)

WEATHER LORE (p. 25)

1. Hopelessly unreliable. No known weather statistics support this one.
2. Good. The woolly fleece referred to here is the fair weather cumulus often associated with a pleasant summer day.
3. Good. In fine weather, early morning inshore mists drift out to sea and disappear or merge with the haze of the heat by noon.
4. Very unreliable. Unsupported by statistics.
5. Good. The brough means the halo caused by a veil of high-level cloud which heralds an approaching depression.
6. Good. After the passing of a depression, although the barometer rises and the weather is brighter, squalls and showers should be anticipated.
7. A bit of a mixture; it depends what you mean by 'red'. A rosy sunset or dawn can be associated with fine weather, but a vivid red sunset can mean rain and a similar sunrise can mean both wind and rain.
8. This is a good reminder that the range and relative movement of the barometer are a good indication of the violence and duration of an approaching spell of bad weather.
9. Not too reliable for anticipating wind direction close to the coast in settled, warm weather where there are strong offshore or onshore breezes.
10. True. Animals and birds are particularly sensitive to changes in the weather system.

LIGHT UP (p. 26)

1. (a) False (b) True (c) True (d) False (e) False (f) True (g) True
(h) True

The term 'not under command' refers to a boat that is unable to manoeuvre (e.g. through loss of steering or engine power, etc.).

2. Both are required to show a white light. Larger ships at anchor may display an additional light at the stern and may also display working lights.

3. True. In some cases (small power-driven craft) the light is combined with the masthead light as an all-round white light. The purpose of the light, however, remains the same – to enable the boat be seen from astern.

4. (a) green over white (b) red over white

5. (d) 7 lights in all:
   all-round green over all-round white
   all-round white over all-round red (hauling in lights)
   red sidelight
   green sidelight
   stern light

6. The towing vessel carries both lights on the same mast, one above the other. The large power-driven vessel carries them on different masts, the after light higher than the for'd light. Viewed from exactly ahead, of course, it would be difficult to identify one from the other, but if the tow exceeds 200 m, a third white light is shown.

7. One all-round white light.

BOSUN'S LOCKER (p. 27)

1. The 7 indicates that they magnify the object seven times, and the 50 indicates the diameter of the object lens in millimetres.

2. Both are associated with practical jokes traditionally played on a merchant ship. Many hours have been spent by first trippers in searching for the keys of the fog locker or asking around the ship for a 'long stand'.

3. Lloyd's Register – the national ship classification society

4. They all measure the altitude of the sun, moon, or stars. The astrolabe was replaced by the backstaff, and the sextant replaced the backstaff.

5. A sailmaker, or a rigger

6. Flotsam is wreckage, whereas jetsam refers to things deliberately thrown overboard.

7. It was designed to enable someone to ascend from a wrecked vessel in order to carry a lifeline ashore.

8. A boathook

9. A drifter. Trawlers are used to catch fish which live near the seabed such as cod, haddock, and sole. Drifters are usually smaller than

trawlers and catch fish that live near the sea surface, such as herrings and mackerel.

10. One-tenth of a sea mile; 600 feet, 200 yards or 100 fathoms

BIRDS OF A FEATHER (p. 28)

E	S	P	R	N	A	C	T	H	O	Q	R	F
K	I	L	E	Q	I	O	P	O	H	T	U	S
I	L	O	P	E	T	R	E	L	N	I	W	F
T	K	V	O	B	T	M	J	I	A	W	E	O
T	C	E	R	A	Z	O	R	B	I	L	L	B
I	E	R	N	O	D	R	E	P	M	E	R	A
W	M	N	L	R	D	A	O	A	R	O	U	F
A	K	C	N	I	E	N	R	T	Y	Z	C	X
K	R	T	N	A	E	T	S	J	B	E	N	W
E	D	S	A	K	B	E	R	A	M	L	U	F
N	M	L	P	O	K	T	S	E	T	U	P	V

1. Fulmar   2. Kittiwake   3. Tern   4. Curlew   5. Kestrel   6. Plover
7. Cormorant   8. Petrel   9. Gannet   10. Razorbill

ANSWERS PART 3

HEAD IN THE CLOUDS (p. 29)

1. . Cirrus – thin high-level cloud meaning good weather. Mare's-tails indicate strong winds at high altitude
2. Cirrocumulus – a 'mackerel' sky with changeable weather
3. Cirrostratus – heralding a depression
4. Altocumulus – thunderstorms may develop if thickening
5. Altostratus – rain on the way

6. Stratocumulus – much drizzle in winter
7. Stratus – drizzle and poor visibility
8. Nimbostratus – steady rain
9. Cumulus – small and puffy, indicates fair weather
10. Cumulonimbus – towering and forbidding clouds bringing squalls, rain, hail, and even thunderstorms

STRIKE A LIGHT (pp. 30 and 31)

1. (b). All of these items, however, may be shown on the chart
2. (a) and (b)
3. (c). Item (a) is a flashing light
4. (b)
5. (d)
6. (c) 12 m or 40′
7. (b). Mean High Water in USA
8. (c)
9. (d). This is often used in connection with sectored lights above
10. (a). Although it can't be relied upon absolutely, it provides quite a good indication of the position and characteristic of the light – a useful early warning.
11. (d)
12. (c). The others are: (a) East, (b) West, (d) North

CHART SYMBOLS 2 (p. 32)

1. (e) Plotted from course steered and distance run from last known position
2. (i) Position line from observing two objects in line with each other. An excellent opportunity to check the magnetic compass, but see the microcomputer program on p. 46 as well
3. (a) Position at the intersection of two or more position lines
4. (f) Position estimated using course steered, distance run, leeway, and the set and drift of the tide or current since last reliable fix
5. (j) Indicates a safe course to avoid a hazard. May use a bearing of an object or a line of soundings
6. (b) The direction in which the tide or current is setting
7. (h) Course steered
8. (d) An estimation of the course actually achieved with regard to the influences listed in item 4 above
9. (g) A line somewhere along which the boat is situated
10. (c) Where time has elapsed between establishing two separate position lines, the first one is transferred up to the second. The transfer is made in the direction of the course made good during the intervening period

RECORD BREAKERS (p. 32)

1. Between Greenwich and Gravesend in 1661. A race held between Charles II and his brother James, Duke of York. The King won.
2. The Cork Harbour Water Club, founded in 1720
3. Marina Del Rey in Los Angeles, California, which has almost 8,000 berths
4. 1,767 sailing boats in a race held in Denmark in 1983
5. The *Bertha*, a dredger designed by Brunel in 1844, is the oldest motor-driven vessel
6. 5,806 gross tons: the *France II*, launched in 1911
7. RMS *Queen Elizabeth* (82,998 GT)
8. She had seven masts
9. 465 nautical miles by the *Champion of the Seas* (2,722 reg tons)
10. 25,000 sq feet or 2,322 sq metres
11. The 5' 10.5" converted barrel *Toniky Nou*, sailed by Eric Peters in 1982–83
12. Spanish: the *Vittoria* in 1519–1522
13. Sir Francis Drake's *Golden Hind* in 1577–1580
14. The *World Gala* of Liberia, an ore/oil carrier – 133,748 GRT
15. The proa (outrigger) *Crossbow II* achieved a speed of 36.04 knots in 1980

JUST A LOAD OF WIND (p. 33)

1. True
2. True
3. False
4. False. This is true in the Northern hemisphere only
5. True
6. False
7. True
8. True – owing to the lower frictional drag of water
9. False. This is a near gale (Force 7)
10. True, according to the Beaufort wind scale terminology

SIGNPOSTS (p. 34)

Position 1: Outfalls, spoil areas, special zones, etc. are usually indicated by special marks in yellow. The yellow buoy at position 7 should be here.

Position 2: The red spar at position 9. The red buoy at position 4 would also be suitable but spars are more likely to be found in channels. In Japan, and North and South America, however, a green spar or buoy would be correct, as these countries use the 'red to starboard' buoyage system.

Position 3: The green spar at position 2

Position 4: The green buoy at position 10
Position 5: The isolated danger mark at position 8
Position 6: The safe water (or mid-channel) mark at position 5
Position 7: Wrecks are treated as any other hazard and are marked in a variety of ways. The East cardinal buoy at position 11 is the solution here. You may have used the isolated danger mark (position 8) but the wreck is rather close to the shore and may not have clear water around it.
Position 8: The South cardinal buoy at position 1
Position 9: The West cardinal buoy at position 6
Position 10: The North cardinal buoy at position 3
Position 11: The red port-hand buoy at position 4

SEATALK 3 (p. 35)

1. To fill (e.g. arming the lead – filling the base of the leadline with tallow in order to obtain a sample of the sea bottom)
2. To haul down on a rope (tricing is the opposite)
3. To tilt
4. To deliberately tip or haul a boat over (e.g. in order to work on or inspect the bottom)
5. To make watertight
6. To beat to windward off a lee shore
7. To finish off a task
8. To carry maximum sail
9. To bind up with rope
10. To bind two objects together
11. To sail too close to the wind
12. To pass rope through an opening (e.g. in a block)
13. To join two pieces of timber
14. To haul a line tight. A method by which one hand pulls on the line whilst the other takes in the slack
15. To fill spaces in the rope prior to covering or parcelling

PEA SOUPER (p. 35)

1. (d) 2. (a) 3. (f) (see note below) 4. (a) 5. (a) 6. (a) 7. (a) 8. (c)
9. (e) (see note below) 10. (b)
Note: If vessel is more than 100 metres long, the bell is followed by a 5 seconds gong placed in the after part of the vessel.

SHAPE UP! (p. 36)

1. (e) 2. (d) 3. (f) 4. (c) 5. (b)
6. (g) 7. (a) 8. (i) 9. (h) and (g) 10. (j)

ATLANTIC CROSSING (p. 36)

1. Tiller extension 2. Bermudan rig 3. Oilskins 4. Rubbing strake (a beading along the outside of the hull to protect against chafing) 5. Kicking strap 6. Strong winds 7. Rowlock 8. Sail hank 9. Mizzen mast 10. Ditchcrawling (cruising in shallow water)

DO THEY MEAN US? (p. 37)

1. (a) 2. (d) 3. (c) 4. (c) 5. (a) 6. (a) 7. (d) 8. (b)

VICTOR HOTEL FOXTROT (pp. 38 and 39)

1. (b)
2. (d)
3. (a). Channel 6 is the international safety channel, channel 22 is used in the USA to contact the Coastguard, and channel 67 is the UK yacht safety communication channel. Channels 6 and 16 are mandatory channels
4. (b). Dual watch (d) means monitoring two frequencies simultaneously
5. False. CB is not monitored by the Coastguard and many sets have only minimal range
6. (a)
7. False. Silence periods may be used for emergency calls.
8. (a) SÉCURITÉ
   (b) MAYDAY
   (c) PAN PAN
9. The position of the vessel. This should be given after the name and could be repeated before the OVER procedure
10. (b)
11. True where there are no language difficulties
12. (a), (b), and (d). (c), 'over and out', must never be used as it is a contradictory term. 'Over' indicates the speaker expects a reply whereas 'out' indicates that the speaker does not anticipate a reply
13. The former indicates that normal working may be resumed whereas the latter indicates that restricted working may be resumed
14. False. There is considerable variation in the regulations from one port to another
15. They are *all* recommended prefixes

TIME AND TIDE (p. 40)

1. False. This results in a spring tide
2. False. Gales and the like can have a considerable effect on the tide
3. True. Approximately 7¼ hours to flood and 5¼ hours to ebb

4. False. Spring tides produce *lower* low tides than neap tides
5. False. In the Pacific Ocean tides are generally of a diurnal nature which means they occur once a day – half the rate of those in the Atlantic Ocean
6. True
7. False. Mixed tides occur when two daily tides vary considerably in height
8. True. A check on any local tide table will verify this
9. True
10. False. It occurs around the 3rd and 4th hours of the tide. A simple rule of thumb is 1/12 in the first and sixth hour, 2/12 in the second and fifth, 3/12 in the third and fourth. A more accurate method is presented in the microcomputer program on p. 47

CHART SYMBOLS 3 (p. 40)

1. Radar reflector
2. Lanby (large automatic navigational buoy)
3. Fixed offshore platform
4. Underwater rock
5. Eddies
6. Stake, perch, withy, or boom
7. Light-vessel
8. Mooring buoy
9. Sewer, outfall pipe
10. Marine radiobeacon
11. Data-collecting buoy (Ocean Data-Acquisition System)
12. Explosive fog signal
13. Morse code fog signal
14. Directional
15. Dolphin (mooring platform)
16. Position approximate
17. Monument
18. Leading
19. Covers
20. Neap tide

NIGHTMARE (p. 41)

Had the radio operator met his end in such a fashion, the contents of his dream would have remained unknown . . .

SEA LAWYER (pp. 42 and 43)

1. (a)
2. (c)
3. True
4. (a) True
   (b) True
   (c) True
   (d) False
   (e) False (they are subject to an increasing range of conservation treaties and agreements)
   (f) True
   (g) True
   (h) False (only internationally agreed forms of b/c are permitted)
5. (d)
6. True
7. False
8. False
9. True
10. (a)
11. False. Though how they secure that right is another problem!
12. True
13. False